Game

Throw the dice and set off. The first kitten home is the winner!

13 Fall in snowdrift and have to be rescued. Go back one space.

14

15

16 Stop by a chestnut seller's fire to warm up. Go back to 12.

12

17

18

19 Climb a tree and see your owner. Jump forward two spaces.

20

21

22 Chased by a rolling snowball. Run back five spaces.

23

24

HOME

£4.20

Printed and Published by D. C. Thomson & Co., Ltd.,
Dundee and London

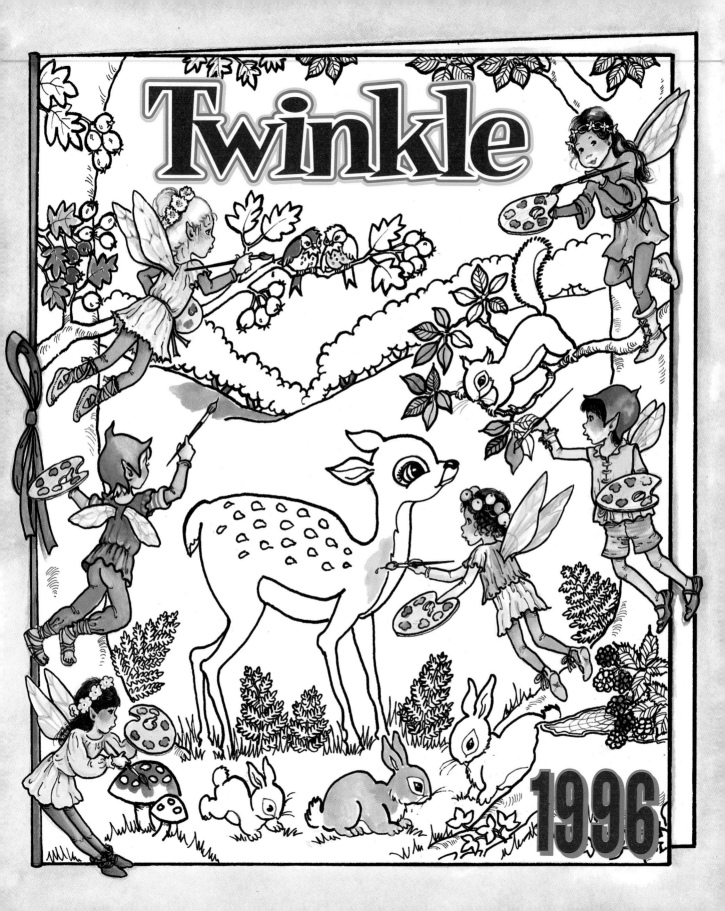

Hello, girls!

This fun-packed, new Twinkle Book is specially for YOU!

It's full of your favourite Twinkle chums — Nurse Nancy, Patch, Silly Milly, Sam and Penny Crayon — AND has lots of terrific new stories, too.

You'll love reading Emily's TV treat, The Runaway Round-up and Up, up and away as well as having a super time with all the games and puzzles.

There are 64 colourful pages for you to enjoy. Have fun!

Love,

Twinkle

Nurse Nancy

1 — On her way to the Dollies Hospital, Nurse Nancy saw a sign for the Christmas pantomime. "I can't wait to see the show," she said excitedly.

2 — At the hospital, Grandad and Colin, the ambulance boy, were already working. "Will you put up the decorations, Nancy?" Grandad asked. "We're busy with some new patients."

3 — The little nurse was chatting to the patients as she decorated the ward, so she didn't see Colin and Grandad secretly bringing in an enormous bundle.

4 — It was only when Nancy heard Colin laugh that she saw him and Grandad put a patient to bed. "Who can that be?" she wondered as they closed the curtains.

5 — Just then, Claire Bright came to collect her toy lamb. "Woolly is as good as new," Nancy told Claire. "I'll tell Grandad you came."

6 — Before Nancy saw Grandad, however, Brian Smith came in. "Is my teddy mended, Nancy?" he asked. But Nancy couldn't find the teddy. "I'll ask Grandad," the little nurse said.

7 — Mr Jingle was nowhere to be found, though. Colin was missing too! "There's only one place left to look," Nancy decided. She went to where the mystery patient lay . . .

8 — . . . and she pulled back the curtains. "Oh!" Nancy cried, and she jumped in surprise. "What is it?" asked Brian. But Nancy could only laugh.

9 — "It's a *horse*!" she giggled when she'd got over the shock. Suddenly, the horse trotted around the ward, kicking a leg out to the side as if it was dancing.

10 — Colin's head popped out of the horse's neck. "It's only us playing tricks on you," he chuckled. "And Grandad is in the other end," Nancy said, smiling.

11 — "Oh, no, I'm not!" called Grandad. "Oh, yes, you are!" answered Nancy, pantomime style. Later, Grandad said the horse's ear had been torn.

12 — "Now he's mended I'll take him to the theatre," Nancy told Grandad. And everyone laughed as the little nurse and the pantomime horse trotted down the street.

Silly Milly

1 — No matter what Silly Milly does, it ends in a muddle. When she sampled perfume for Mum's Christmas, Milly squirted it into the assistant's eye.

2 — Next, Milly went to the Men's Department to get something for Dad. But, as she was being served, her bag caught on to a dummy's arm and pulled it to the floor. *Crash!*

3 — "You silly girl!" called an assistant. "Oops, sorry," said Milly, blushing, as she freed her bag. "Maybe I should go to another department," she thought wisely.

4 — "I know. I'll buy biscuits for Gran," Milly decided. But she took a tin from the bottom — and the whole display fell. "Oh, crumbs," cried Milly.

5 — She rushed off, saying to herself, "I'll just get a toy for cousin Charlie." But, in her hurry, she tripped over a cable. "Aagh!" she wailed.

6 — Other children were crying, too. It was an electric cable that Milly had pulled out and now the display toys wouldn't work. "Out!" ordered the manager. "You're just trouble!"

7 — "I didn't buy any gifts," Milly sadly told Mum. "Never mind," said Mum kindly. "I have just what you need here. Come indoors."

8 — She gave Milly a Christmas catalogue. "You choose the presents and *I'll* buy them for you," Mum told Milly. "Sounds like the best way to shop — for *me*, anyway," said Milly.

Puzzle time presents

The ribbon's falling from Patty's present! Which end must she pick up?

Join the dots to find what Tracy is carrying home to decorate!

RENEJIFN

OLISUE

LATEZBIHE

ANJANO

Unscramble the names on the labels to find who the parcels are for.

Rearrange the first letters of the items from Mo's bag to find where she's been.

The Runaway Round-up

CHARLIE the pony wished he could be a Wild West pony and go out rounding up cattle. One day, Charlie's wish nearly came true.

He and his owner, Lisa, were trotting through the village. It was usually very quiet in the village, with no excitement at all!

But today, there was *great* excitement! Today, there was a cattle market. Inside a fence in the village square, cows and baby calves were being bought and sold.

Suddenly, a brown and white cow with a brown calf broke loose! They went racing through the village street! The cow roared, "Moo! Moo!" while the calf went, "Ma-a-a-! Ma-a-a!"

"Hoi! Come back!" cried a farmer, and he chased after them.

But he couldn't catch them.

2 — Charlie couldn't believe his luck!

"Runaway cattle!" he whinnied.

And Charlie took off after the cow and calf.

Lisa was so surprised, she pulled on Charlie's reins for him to halt.

"Whoa, Charlie!" she cried.

But Charlie had no intention of obeying Lisa and spoiling his chance! He galloped after the runaway animals.

3 — Down the street ran the cow and her calf, followed by Lisa on Charlie, then the farmer.

Crash! The cow charged into a stall outside the greengrocer's shop! Fruit and vegetables scattered all over the place!

Oranges and apples tumbled on to the road and potatoes burst out of their bags, bouncing everywhere!

The brown and white cow gave a loud roar, but kept on going! Her little calf went after her, calling loudly.

Next came Charlie. When he came to the spilled fruit and vegetables, he rose up in the air like a bird . . . then landed on a pile of apples, making his hooves skid under him!

Poor Lisa had to hang on tightly.

4 — As Charlie saw the cow and her calf escaping, he made a quick recovery. He neighed, reared up on his hind legs, then took off again.

"Charlie! Charlie!" Lisa yelled. "What's got into you? Whoa! Whoa!"

But Charlie didn't listen to Lisa. In his head, he could hear the music that they always played in the Wild West films when the horses' hooves were thundering along. *Boom, boo-de-boom . . .*

Now the cow and her calf were reaching the end of the village. They couldn't go as quickly as Charlie, though. He was fast catching up with them!

5 — Just then, Lisa saw the cow and her calf run through a brood of hens.

"*Squawk! Squawk! Squawk!*" they screeched, and they scattered in all directions.

Then Charlie raced amongst them.

"*Squawk! Squawk! Squawk!*" they went again.

One of the hens got such a fright, it flew on to Charlie's back and perched behind Lisa.

Charlie neighed happily. This was great fun! He didn't care about Lisa calling "Whoa" or the hen clucking and squawking. All he cared about was his hooves thundering along to the music in his head, *boom, boo-de-boom,* and the thought of rounding up the cattle.

6 — Suddenly, the sight of the river made Charlie sense that the cow and her calf were in great danger. The river was high and the cattle were heading straight for it.

Charlie put on another spurt and, just in the nick of time, he overtook the two animals. He planted himself between them and the river, then he neighed and snorted. He reared up and waved his front hooves in the air.

"Squawk!" clucked the hen on his back, and it flew off.

"Charlie!" shrieked Lisa as she slid down the saddle.

The brown and white cow got a terrible fright, too, and she turned away from the river and trotted back the way she had come, with her calf following.

The farmer caught up with them all and he led the cattle home.

7 — When Charlie and Lisa reached the village, a crowd was waiting.

"We thought we were in the Wild West!" someone said.

Charlie *was* pleased.

Later, the farmer gave Lisa a huge bag of apples for Charlie.

Charlie was very pleased with the apples. He was even more pleased, though, when Lisa got him a cowboy hat.

Now he felt like a *real* Wild West pony!

1 — It was early Christmas and Paula Perkins and her mummy and daddy were decorating the house. Patch, Paula's kitten, loved to try to open the parcels.

2 — When he thought no one was looking, the cheeky puss found a parcel that smelled extra good. He opened it. Inside were his favourite fish biscuits!

3 — No matter how many times Paula stopped him, Patch *wouldn't* leave the parcels alone. Paula decided something would have to be done.

4 — She thought of a clever plan and Mummy and Daddy helped her put it into action. "I'll put *this* parcel where Patch can't miss it," said Paula.

Can you find eight apples hidden on these pages?

5 — And when Patch touched the parcel, as Paula knew he would, what a surprise he got. It sprang to life and began chasing him round and round the room!

6 — Paula finally stopped the runaway parcel. Inside was a clockwork mouse for Patch! "I hope you'll leave the presents alone, now," laughed Paula.

WEE Benny's sweet, but seldom neat,
He's full of fun and joy.
He's grubby, friendly, naughty, cute,
Like any little boy. He's . . .

My Baby Brother

BEN just loves anything that's *red*,
His favourite colour's that.
Out playing in the snow, he'll choose
His bright *red* bobble hat.

He's got a football jersey, too —
As *red* as *red* can be.
"I can score goals when I wear this!"
The rascal calls to me.

Red cherries at the market stall
He simply does adore.
There's nothing left but stalks and stones
When we get home once more!

All fire engines are bright *red*.
Ben claps his hands with glee.
"I'll be a fireman when I'm grown!"
He shouts excitedly.

He's got a bucket that is *red* —
  He builds sandcastles tall,
And then we stick a smart *red* flag
  Right on the top of all.

The garden bird Ben loves the best?
  It's one that comes a-bobbin'.
Well, can you guess which one it is?
  Of course, the *red, red* robin!

When strawberry days are here again,
  Ben loves to come along.
He picks the biggest, *reddest* ones,
  And sings a little song.

When jolly Christmas comes around,
  Ben thinks that it is great.
Red holly berries on the trees,
  Red crackers by his plate!

What a to-do at Sunnygate Zoo

WHAT a to-do there was at Sunnygate Zoo one day. Lots of baby animals had just been born and every mummy animal thought that *her* baby was the prettiest.

"My Koo-Koo is so cute," said Mrs Koala.

"But Jemima's *so* graceful," boasted Mrs Giraffe.

"You have to admit that Suzy is the most beautiful baby," Mrs Sealion sighed.

"Oh, no, she's not!" cried Mrs Lion. "My cub, Cuthbert, is!"

To stop the arguments, the animals decided to have a "Beautiful Baby Contest." Mr Sunny, the keeper, was to be the judge.

As the mummies prepared their babies for the contest, each one was secretly sure that *her* baby would win.

Mrs Penguin proudly tied a pink ribbon round baby Pippa's neck. But Mrs Elephant was shocked when little Edgar soaked Mr Sunny with his bath water.

"Edgar!" she trumpeted loudly. "That's naughty! You won't win like that!"

"No matter *who* wins, the other mothers will be offended," thought Mr Sunny. "What can I do?"

The zoo-keeper decided to ask his daughter, Jenny, to help.

"It's very difficult," agreed Jenny as she watched Henry Hippo rolling about in the mud. "Henry's a very happy little hippo. He could win a prize for 'the *happiest* baby'."

"That's true," said her daddy, "but he's not really *cuddly*, is he?"

"I know!" answered Jenny. "Why don't you give them *all* a prize?"

And so at two o'clock, Mr Sunny gathered the animals together to announce the winners.

"Jemima Giraffe wins the prize for being the *tallest* baby," he began, "and Koo-Koo Koala wins for being the *cuddliest*."

Then Jenny said, "Cuthbert Cub wins for having the loudest roar, while Suzy Sealion wins for being the *sweetest* baby."

Before long, *all* the babies were wearing a winner's rosette for something or other. Everyone was *so* happy, the zoo had a lovely big party to celebrate!

Mum knows best

1

BASIL was an elephant
    Who wouldn't eat his greens.
At breakfast, lunch and dinner,
    He created awful scenes.
Most of us like egg on toast
    But Basil wouldn't try,
He wanted sweets and chocolate
    Or he would start to cry.

2

For lunch, his Mum would pile his plate
    With salad, beans and meat,
But Basil wanted toffee,
    So he'd scowl and stamp his feet.
At supper time, he'd play about
    And fiddle with his food,
Despite his mother telling him
    It was *extremely* rude.

3

As time went by, a change was seen
    In Basil, foolish fellow.
His tusks and teeth, once shiny white,
    Began to turn quite yellow.
Across his face appeared a rash
    Of spots, bright red and sore
And Basil wasn't growing
    Very quickly any more.

4

To Mum he said, "Oh dear, oh dear,
    Whatever shall I do?"
"Well, eat up all your food, my boy,
    Just like I told you to."
So Basil drank his milk and juice
    And ate up all his food
And quite soon he felt well again —
    As Mum had said he would.

Sam

SHONA MACGREGOR has a clever sheepdog called Sam. They live on a farm in the Scottish Highlands.

One day, when they were out walking, they came across huge footprints in the snow.

"Look at *these*, Sam," cried Shona with a gasp. "I've never seen anything like them before. I wonder what sort of animal can have made them?"

Sam sniffed the tracks and gave a low growl.

2 — As the chums made their way back to the farm, a mist came down.

"Don't get too far ahead of me," Shona warned Sam.

Then, suddenly, a strange, dark shape moved through the trees ahead of them!

"What was *that*?" the little girl cried in amazement.

3 — Shona soon had her answer. When she arrived safely home, she found Mr MacGregor watching TV — and on the screen was a picture of a large, brown bear.

"It has escaped from a film set nearby," explained Mr MacGregor. "They've had teams out looking for it all day but the mist has hindered the search and there's been no sign of it."

"Oh, yes, there has!" cried Shona. "*That* must be what Sam and I nearly bumped into!"

4 — Mr MacGregor wasted no time in phoning the police and it wasn't long before the bear's owner arrived with the search team.

Shona retraced her steps and led the party back to where she and Sam had been earlier.

"He walked in front of us, going into those trees," Shona explained to them.

"Well, I'm sure he won't be far away," the owner said. "He's not accustomed to the wilds and will probably be feeling quite lost."

5 — Sure enough, before they'd gone much further, the shaggy beast lumbered out of the trees and headed straight for Mr MacGregor's sheep which were grazing nearby.

Fearing that the bear was looking for a tasty snack, Sam raced off towards the huge creature.

"Oh, Sam! Do be careful!" cried Shona. "You won't stand a chance if the bear lashes out at you."

But the sheepdog was determined to protect his flock and raced on.

6 — What a surprise Shona got, however, when Sam reached the bear. It sat up and began to clap its hands!

Its owner *did* laugh.

"I didn't get the chance to tell you," he explained with a smile, "but Hector is a big softy. He wouldn't have been going to *harm* the sheep, he'd have wanted to *play* with them. Having got lost, he'd be lonely!"

Indeed, Hector was so glad to have been found that he could hardly wait to clamber into his cosy travelling home.

7 — "Thanks for your help in finding Hector," called the bear's owner. "He wouldn't have been able to look after himself properly in the wilds."

And, the following week, a parcel arrived for Shona — from Hector! In it was a special "thank you" present, a cuddly teddy bear!

"I'll treasure it forever," the little girl told her faithful four-footed chum.

And Sam wagged his tail in reply.

Snowtime

Find six differences between these two snowmen.

Only two stars are exactly the same. Can you spot them?

Lead Rosie home through the maze.

Name the plants Rosie is holding. Their names are jumbled up.

O L H
Y L
O Y

V I Y
Y

S O E T T
I L M E

puzzles

There are nine things in the wordsearch below which can be found on these pages. The words read up and down, back and forwards.

Which wisp of smoke is coming from the chimney?

A   B   C

S	H	L	T	S	K	Y
R	O	B	I	N	F	T
A	U	E	E	O	B	O
T	S	A	H	W	P	O
S	E	R	T	A	C	B

What is the odd one out on the sledge?

Chocs.

ANSWER:-
Tie. The others all start with "c".

ANSWERS:-
Stars, cat, bear, tie, boot, robin, sky, house, snow.

Cuddles and Co.

1 — When Nadia's neighbour, Mrs Smith, came to visit, Cuddles the dog was very pleased to see her. He jumped up as she opened the door.

2 — "Down, boy!" Nadia scolded her pet. "It's nice to get such a welcome, but I don't want paw prints all over my coat," added Mrs Smith. Cuddles *was* sorry.

3 — Later, Mrs Smith was reading when Midge and Tiny both tried to sit on her knee. "I've often wanted a pet, but I don't think I want all this bother," she sighed.

4 — After Mrs Smith went home, the cats began to play together, tugging at a cushion. "Be careful!" wuffed Cuddles. "You'll tear it with your sharp claws!"

5 — He tried to pull it away from the naughty cats, but it was the wrong thing to do. The cushion suddenly ripped open, spilling stuffing all over the floor.

6 — But instead of being angry, Mummy realised that it had just been an accident. "Let's do something with this cushion now that it's torn," she said.

7 — Mummy stitched the cushion material into three separate shapes and Nadia helped her put the stuffing into each shape. "Soon be finished," said Mummy.

8 — Next day, Nadia and Mummy had a lovely surprise for Mrs Smith — toys which looked like Cuddles, Midge and Tiny. "My own little pets!" she laughed. "How lovely!"

Use your paints or crayons to complete this colourful scene.

Emily's TV treat

EMILY ELEPHANT *loved* watching television.

"You'll have square eyes soon," Mummy Elephant laughed.

"I wish *I* could be on TV," Emily sighed as she copied the dancers on her set.

"Maybe you will be, *one* day," her mummy replied. "But right *now*, I'd like you to take this basket of food to old Mrs Lion. She has broken her leg and can't get out."

"Oh, poor Mrs Lion," Emily said. "I'll take my Twinkle magazine, too. That will cheer her up."

2 — Emily was a kind little elephant. She tidied Mrs Lion's house, then made her a nice cup of tea and a sandwich.

Afterwards, Emily stayed for a chat with Mrs Lion. As they talked, Mrs Lion asked Emily what she would like to be when she grew up.

"I'm going to be a television star," Emily answered.

And her eyes misted over as she dreamed of being a famous dancer.

"Just think," she told Mrs Lion, "everywhere I go, people will be queuing up for my autograph."

Mrs Lion smiled and asked, "Have you gone to the television studios in town?"

"Why didn't *I* think of that?" Emily murmured excitedly. "I'll pop along to the television studios now and ask how I can become a TV star."

As soon as Mrs Lion was comfortable, Emily set off.

3 — As she was passing Mr Camel's garden, Emily heard him call to her.

"Emily, would you hold this fence post straight for me, please?" he asked.

Emily hesitated for a moment. She was desperate to get to the television studios before lunch-time. She could see Mr Camel needed some help, though, so she held the fence post for him.

"That was kind of you," he said, when it was done. "Here's ten pence."

Emily thanked him and hurried off towards the TV studios.

4 — Emily hadn't gone very far when she heard someone saying, "Oh, dear me!"

It was Grandma Panda and, when she saw Emily, she said, "Please can you reach my sheet with your long trunk? The wind blew it on to the roof."

So Emily rescued the flyaway sheet and Grandma Panda gave her ten pence.

"Thank you," Emily replied politely and she hurried on.

5 — By the duck pond, Emily heard Dorothy Duck quacking loudly. She ran over to see what was wrong.

"Can I help?" Emily offered.

"Oh, please," Dorothy quacked anxiously. "My baby has fallen down a deep hole and I can't get him out."

The duckling was cheeping loudly. Emily curled her trunk very gently around him, lifted him up, and popped him down beside his mummy.

"Oh, thank you!" quacked Dorothy.

"You're welcome," Emily smiled.

6 — Just then, Emily realised it was lunch-time.

"Perhaps I can go to the television studios after lunch," she told herself. "But now I'll pop into the cake shop and buy Mummy her favourite cream cake with my twenty pence."

As Emily reached the cake shop, Mr Bear the baker came rushing out, shouting, "Help! Help! The kitchen is on fire!"

7 — Emily could see the shop filling with smoke.

"Call the fire brigade!" she told Mr Bear.

Next, she rushed back to the duck pond, filled up her trunk with water, dashed into the cake shop and sprayed the water over the fire. Back and forth she went from the duck pond to the cake shop and, by the time the fire brigade arrived, the fire was out.

8 — Everyone thought Emily was very brave. Her photograph was in all the newspapers and, best of all, she was interviewed on television. Afterwards, she was shown around the studios.

"Well, you got your wish," Mummy Elephant smiled as she tucked a happy, but very tired, Emily in her bed that night. "Was it as exciting as you thought it would be?" Mummy asked.

But Emily didn't reply. She was fast asleep.

c

1 — Wendy Wilson has a *most* unusual chum — Winkle, a 300-year-old witch. Despite the difference in their ages, they were the best of friends.

2 — One day, Wendy was concerned to see Winkle crying her eyes out while reading a letter. "It's from my cousin, Grizelda," said Winkle. "I haven't seen her for a hundred and fifty years!"

3 — "Why don't you invite Grizelda here for a holiday?" suggested Wendy, kindly. "What about your parents?" said Winkle. "Won't they mind?" "Let's ask them," said Wendy.

4 — Wendy's parents readily agreed and a few days later, Grizelda arrived. The two cousins were overjoyed to see each other. "We have so much to talk about," said Winkle.

5 — And the ladies began catching up on a hundred and fifty years of gossip! "Did you know I was voted 'Witch of the Year' for the hundredth time?" boasted Grizelda.

6 — When they all sat down at the dinner table, Grizelda carried on talking. No one else could get a word in. "She does go on, doesn't she?" whispered Dad.

7 — At bedtime, an exhausted Winkle sank wearily into her bed. But when Wendy peeped in later, Grizelda was *still* talking. "Poor Winkle!" thought Wendy.

8 — Next morning, everyone was amazed Grizelda was *still* chatting. "Now I remember why I haven't seen her for a hundred and fifty years," groaned Winkle. "She'll have to go!"

9 — Wendy realised something had to be done to make Grizelda *want* to leave. After much thought, she came up with a solution. "I'll try anything," said Winkle."

10 — . . . "Right, Wendy, I'm here at school as you asked," whispered Winkle. "What do I have to do?" "Put a spell on the headmaster to put our idea in his head," said Wendy.

11 — That evening, Wendy announced, "Our school is holding a sponsored silence tomorrow. I've entered all of us. You'll have to pay five pounds every time you speak."

12 — That did it! The thought of a whole day without speaking was too much for Grizelda and she was off! "'Bye!" called Winkle. "Come again — in another hundred and fifty years!"

The winter fairy

EARLY one very cold morning, a little fairy peeped out from under the bed covers.

"Has it been snowing, I wonder?" she thought.

Sure enough, the ground was covered in a fresh, fluffy layer of snow. That made the fairy very happy because she was Winnie, the winter fairy.

"I must keep the icicles polished and the snowdrops dusted too," she said.

Winnie flitted this way and that, waving her magic wand. When she was finished, she came upon Danny Dormouse curled up in a cosy bed of leaves.

"Won't you come out and play with me?" asked Winnie.

But the only reply was a grunt.

2 — Winnie tried to waken Danny once more, but the sleepy dormouse just turned over and said, "Leave me alone. It's too cold to come out to play."

"Ah, well," sighed Winnie. "I'll just have to find someone else to play with."

She saw Robbie Redbreast nearby.

"Will you please play in the snow with me?" asked Winnie very nicely.

"I'm sorry," chirped Robbie. "I have to look for food. Perhaps later."

3 — The little fairy was still looking for a playmate when she thought of something.

"I can't *find* anyone to play with, so I'll just have to *make* someone," she said with a giggle.

What *did* she mean?

Well, Winnie rolled a large ball of snow and shaped it like a body. Then she put a small snowball on top for a head. Winnie added straw for hair and two leaves like fairies' wings. She even gave her little snow fairy a face.

"There," said Winnie, looking pleased with her work. "You're really rather pretty. I think I'll call you Snowdrop."

4 — Jack Frost had been watching Winnie putting together her snowy playmate.

"Let's make your snow friend come to life," he told her.

He breathed his icy breath over Snowdrop and next moment, her eyes sparkled and she began to move, stiffly at first. Then she fluttered her leafy wings and said, "Hello!"

Winnie was delighted.

"I really *can* play with her now," she cried with excitement. "Thank you so much, Jack!"

And the two new friends flew off into the woods to have some fun together. Snowdrop was thrilled by all the things that Winnie showed her. Winnie also taught her how to play hide and seek, which her new chum loved.

5 — When it was warmer, Winnie took Snowdrop to meet her friends. Danny Dormouse was awake and he came out of his leafy bed to greet Snowdrop.

"Nice to meet you," he called.

Robbie Redbreast had fed his family and chirped a cheerful, "How are you?"

A friendly squirrel waved to the two fairies before scurrying up a tree, back to his cosy nest.

"What lovely friends you have!" cried Snowdrop. "Thank you for making me your friend, too, Winnie!"

How many crackers can you count? Then colour in this pretty picture.

Match each cat with what goes with its costume.

Can you find which two of these cats are identical?

Happy Christmas

Which cat is holding the gift tag ribbon?

These pictures look the same but there are six differences. Can you find them?

Up, up and away . . . !!

BELLA the umbrella was glad it was raining. The weather had been dry for a long time and Bella had been left, folded up, under the stairs.

"Come on, Bella," said Sarah, the little girl who owned her. "We're going out!"

It was very windy and the wind blew and howled round street corners. People battled against it, clutching their hats.

2 — Mum and Sarah were going to visit Mum's friend. When they arrived, they left their umbrellas outside on her porch.

"Let's open them out and perhaps they'll dry while we're inside," said Mum. "They'll be safe here."

But Mum was wrong!

The wind blew round the porch and Bella, being small and light, was lifted up into the air and blown down the street.

The mischievous wind dropped Bella in a field beside a fast flowing stream where a frantic squeaking noise made her jump.

It was Mr Mouse and his family.

"Can you help us, please?" asked Mr Mouse. "We need to move farther up the field and we have to cross this stream. My babies are very tired . . ."

Bella thought — and then she turned herself upside down, so that she looked like a boat.

"Hop in!" she said.

3 — The mouse family jumped aboard, and the umbrella took off across the water.

The mice thought their ride in Bella was great fun.

"I think that's far enough now," said Mr Mouse, after a few minutes. "Jump out, everyone!"

Soon, they were all safely out on the other side of the bank.

"Thank you very much!" they squeaked to Bella.

But next moment, the wind was up to its tricks again. Bella was lifted up and blown across Farmer Brown's field. She bumped and bounced across the ground and then came to a sudden halt.

Bella could hear someone snuffling miserably. Looking up, she saw a very sad and tattered scarecrow.

4 — "Oh, dear!" wailed the scarecrow. "The water's running off my hat and I'm standing in a puddle! I'm sure I've got a cold . . . atchoo!"

Just then, he spotted Bella.

"Why!" he exclaimed, "you're just what I need. A jolly brolly to keep me dry. How lucky!"

And he picked up Bella and held her over his head.

"That's better!" he declared. "Now it can rain as hard as it likes!"

5 — At last, it stopped raining and the sun began to peep through the clouds. Bella suddenly heard footsteps coming along the path.

"Look, Mum! There's my umbrella!"

Bella knew the voice. It was Sarah's.

"I wonder how it got here!" cried Mum. "We'd better tell Farmer Brown."

"I've been searching everywhere for Bella," Sarah told the farmer.

"I can't understand how my scarecrow got hold of your umbrella," the farmer said, handing it back to Sarah.

"Thank you," beamed Sarah, giving Bella a shake and folding her down.

6 — They said goodbye, and as the farmer walked away, he turned and called to them.

"I've just had an idea," he joked. "Do you think my scarecrow found your umbrella and thought it would keep him dry?"

Sarah and Mum began to laugh.

And as they walked away, they felt sure they heard the scarecrow chuckle — or was it Bella?

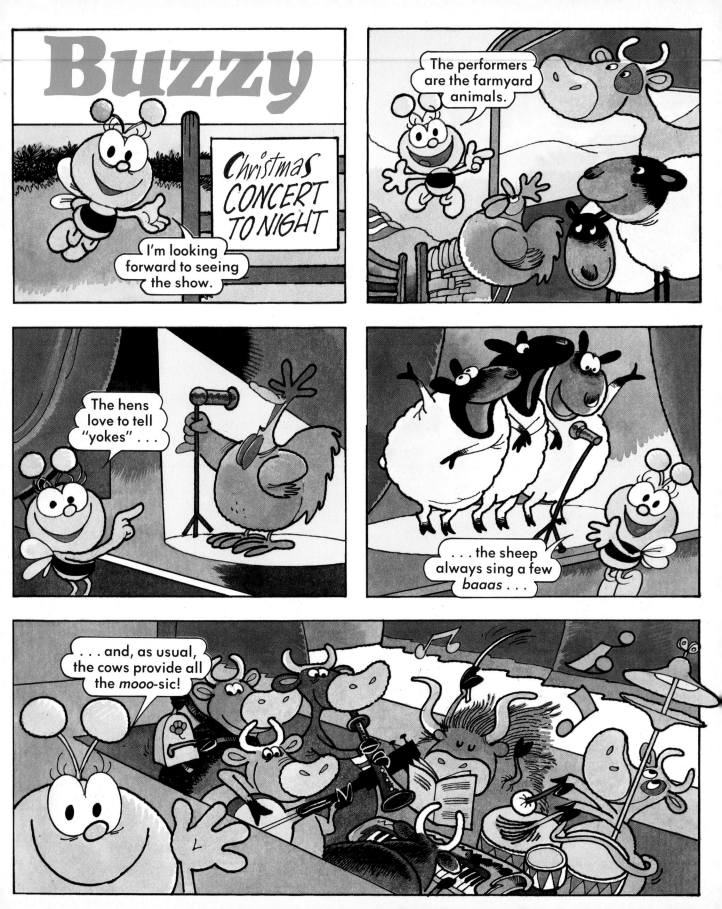

Fairy Fay

1 — For weeks, Fairy Fay had been busy making Christmas presents for all her Fairyland friends. When everything was ready, she sat down to wrap them.

2 — The little fairy tied up all the parcels neatly and carefully. She wanted them to look nice. "I hope everyone likes what I've made for them," she thought.

3 — The finishing touch was a label on each saying, "Do not open until December 25th". "That should stop them opening their presents before Christmas," said Fay.

4 — Then Fay heard carol singing outside. She opened the door to find four of her chums standing in the freezing cold. They were so cold, they could hardly sing!

5 — "M-my teeth are ch-chattering!" said Eddie Elf. "I'm going home for a hot drink." But Fairy Fay had a better idea. "Come inside," she told Fairy Ivy, Fairy Pansy, Eddie and Paul Pixie.

6 — The little carol singers were *most* surprised when Fay went to her Christmas tree and brought out four parcels. "These are for you," she said.

7 — "But it's not Christmas Day yet," cried Ivy. "I know," replied Fay, "but you need these right now." She had knitted them all cosy scarves with hats and mitts.

8 — Now that they were warmly wrapped up, the foursome were happy to sing more carols in the snow. "Have some hot chocolate before you go!" called Fay.

Penny Crayon

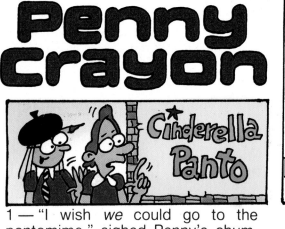

1 — "I wish *we* could go to the pantomime," sighed Penny's chum, Dennis. "No problem!" cried Penny.

2 — Whatever she drew became *real*, so the little artist drew a Fairy Godmother, who waved her wand and cried, "You *shall* go to the ball!"

3 — "No — wait! *I'm* not Cinderella!" Penny protested. But, in a flash, she and Dennis were wearing fancy ballgowns!

4 — "I don't want to wear a *dress,*" Dennis wailed. "Make her change it." But, by then, the Fairy Godmother had run off.

5 — Next, the dotty fairy spotted a huge Christmas pudding. "It's not a pumpkin, but it will do," she cried.

6 — With a twinkle of her wand, the pudding was changed into a *coach.* "Now to find something for horses," the Fairy Godmother cried.

7 — "She thinks she's in *'Cinderella'*," Penny realised. "I'll have to rub her out before she causes more trouble."

8 — But before Penny could begin, the theatre manager appeared. "Our Fairy Godmother is ill. Will *you* take her place?" he asked.

9 — So Penny and Dennis *did* get to the pantomime after all, as the Fairy Godmother's special guests!

Tree toppers

Here are some ideas for Christmas tree decorations, using white balls from craft shops.

To make a snowman or king, stick a small ball on top of a bigger ball to give you a head and body. Use scraps of material or coloured card for clothes, hair and the snowman's broom, then colour the faces with felt pens. If you'd like your decorations to stand, make feet from card and stick them to the body.

A robin and soldier can be made by colouring a ball and adding wings and a tail from card and a hat from material.

A simple card star shape makes a lovely Santa when you stick red fur fabric to it. Decorate with tape and cotton wool as shown.

Two pieces of fur fabric in a stocking shape can be stapled together down the sides, leaving the top open to allow a tube of sweets to fit in. Edge the top with cotton wool.

To top your tree, make a fairy using a tiny paper ball for the head and braid for hair. Bind pipe cleaners for a body, give her a crepe skirt and finish with a lace doily.

Loops of thread can be sewn to the heads to hang your tree toppers from the tree.

Santa surprise

TO make this Santa surprise or advent chimney, you will need 24 empty matchboxes, 24 paper fasteners, cotton wool, strong gum, thin card, felt pens and poster paint. Glue the empty matchbox covers together as shown here. Add five more layers on top.

Make a base from card and stick your matchbox chimney to it. Cut out the Santa here and glue him to thin card. Bend along the dotted line and fix him to the chimney top, supporting him at the back with a small L-shaped piece of card. Paint your chimney and Santa's back red, then, when dry, decorate with cotton wool. Push paper fasteners through each matchbox and pop little presents into the chimney "bricks".

This Santa surprise is perfect for a Christmas party. Just pull out a "brick" to find a gift.

D

Wally Woodpecker's new home

MRS WOODPECKER decided she'd like to live somewhere smarter.

So, after breakfast, Wally Woodpecker went off in search of a new home. Before long, he noticed a pretty tree.

"This would be perfect," he thought.

And he began to peck out a large hole with his beak. *Drrr! Drrr!*

2 — Suddenly, a very cross-looking owl peered down at him.

"Do you mind?" Oswald Owl hooted. "I'm trying to get some sleep up here."

"Oh! Did I wake you?" Wally asked.

"Yes, you did," the sleepy owl grumbled. "This is a *quiet* area."

"Oh, dear!" Wally thought. "I *am* rather noisy. Perhaps I'd better look for another place to live."

And he flew off to find another tree.

3 — Soon Wally found somewhere else and he hammered away with his beak again. *Drrr! Drrrr!*

Just then, dozens of acorns fell.

"Ouch!" cried Wally as they hit his head.

Sybil Squirrel peeped out of the tree.

"You're shaking my store of nuts from my tree!" she called.

"Sorry," Wally replied, and he helped Sybil pick up all the nuts.

"You can't live here," Sybil told him. "I need this tree for my winter larder!"

"All right," Wally sighed. "I'll move."

4 — Wally Woodpecker flew off again.

"House-hunting isn't as easy as I thought," he said to himself.

Later, Wally spotted a lovely cherry tree at the other end of the forest.

"I'll just check no one's living here before I start," he thought.

The woodpecker flew round and round the tree, but there was no sign of anyone. He bored the trunk. *Drrr! Drrr!*

Suddenly, a squeaky voice called out — but Wally didn't know where from.

"Down here!" called the voice, and Wally saw Maurice Mole.

"Stop hammering!" Maurice called. "You've made my new tunnel collapse."

And he pointed to a trail of flattened molehills coming from the tree.

"I give up," groaned Wally.

When Wally told Mrs Woodpecker there would be no new house, she decided to decorate instead.

Just then, Oswald, Sybil and Maurice arrived and said sorry for being so rude.

5 — "Perhaps we can help you decorate," they offered.

So everyone got busy and, when the house was finished, Mrs Woodpecker was *very* pleased with the results.

"It's just like having a new home," she smiled. "I'm glad we didn't move after all!"

Patsy Panda

1 — Patsy was at the ice rink watching her chum, Basil Bear, skating in a contest.

2 — Basil skated very well. "Wow!" cried Patsy. "He's scored full marks!"

3 — "I wish *I* could skate," thought the little panda on her way home.

4 — Suddenly, Patsy slipped on ice. "Help! I can't stop!" she yelled as she gathered speed.

5 — She slipped and slithered down the hill with her arms waving, trying to balance.

6 — At the bottom of the hill, Patsy zoomed round the corner and grabbed hold of a lamp post to slow her down. She flew right round it!

7 — "Nice skating!" said Tim Tiger, laughing. He took down his shop number. "I'll give you five point seven marks!" he joked.

8 — "Thanks!" called Patsy as she slipped on another icy patch. *Splat!* She fell in the snow.

9 — As she picked herself up, the little panda found herself among her mouse chums who were trying to ski, without much success. "We're not very good at this!" cried Monty Mouse.

10 — "Let's go and see Tim Tiger in his ski shop," said Patsy with a smile. "I think he'll have what I'm looking for." The mice followed her.

11 — Patsy bought a pair of long skis and climbed back up the hill with them. "Now for your skiing lesson!" she told the mice.

12 — They *were* puzzled. At the top of the slope, Patsy strapped on the skis and told the mice to jump on, too! There was room for everyone!

13 — "This is the safest way to go home," the little panda said. "And you can hitch a ride!" All Patsy's sliding had been good practice!

Polly

1 — Out walking in Snowland one day, Polly Penguin noticed that everyone she met looked miserable. "It's these long, dark winter days," thought Polly.

2 — Polly's journey took her past the theatre. There, she saw something which gave her an idea. "Are these lights being thrown out?" she asked.

3 — The lights *were* being thrown out and Polly was told she could take them. "Can't think why you want them," said Mr Walrus. "They're very old-fashioned."

4 — The next day, everyone in Snowland received a letter. "Polly's having a party," said Mrs Polar Bear. "We've to wear our *summer* clothes," said Mr Walrus.

5 — On the day of the party, everyone turned up wearing their brightest summer clothes as Polly had asked. And what a wonderful sight met their eyes!

6 — Thanks to the old lights, the room was warm and had a bright glow. "I thought we'd have a picnic and pretend it's summer," laughed Polly.

Tricky treats

Only two of these mince pies are exactly the same. Find them, then "cook" them with your crayons.

Find the following words in this tasty cookbook wordsearch —
CAKE   JELLY   PUDDING   TURKEY

Yum, yum! Lead Jo through the maze to reach the delicious party jelly.

Join the cranberries to find the treat that's been prepared for Christmas dinner!

Jean Genie

1 — Gemma Jones has her very own genie, Slaphappy. One day, Gemma's mum said she was tired of cooking.

2 — "I'll ask Slaphappy to cook for a week," said Gemma. And she slapped her back pocket, making her genie appear.

3 — "Can we have 'Toad in the Hole'?" asked Gemma. "Easy as pie!" answered Slaphappy.

4 — "Your *dish* is my command," he joked. But, instead of sausages in batter, the genie conjured up a fat toad, croaking noisily.

5 — When Gemma and Mum asked for Hot Dogs, Slaphappy produced two hot "sausage" dogs! "That's not what we meant," groaned Gemma.

6 — "You're no use at cooking," Gemma scolded her genie. "I'll try again," said Slaphappy.

7 — But, when he tried Welsh Rarebit, Slaphappy "cooked up" a rabbit from Wales. "Welsh Rarebit is cheese on toast!" Gemma told him, chuckling.

8 — "Ask for something simple," demanded the genie. So Gemma ordered boiled eggs and soldiers.

9 — Mum and Gemma sat down at the table and Slaphappy put their boiled eggs in front of them. "Perfect," said Mum.

10 — But then some soldiers marched in! "I should have known he'd bring *real* soldiers," Mum said, crossly.

11 — "I'm tired of your half-baked spells! Get everyone out!" Mum shouted. And Slaphappy did it.

12 — "Now *I'll* conjure us up a meal," said Mum. And she made a Shepherd's Pie — without a shepherd in sight!

The Christmas tree

IT was the day before Christmas, and all the animals in the forest were very busy.

Matilda Mouse was happily wrapping up the last of her Christmas presents.

"Hannah Hedgehog is certain to love this!" she exclaimed as she struggled to roll a bright red and white woolly scarf into some pretty green tissue paper.

Carefully, she wrote the tag out in her best handwriting.

2 — "The presents *do* look lovely sitting on my polished kitchen table," she smiled. "But what I really need is a Christmas tree to put them under."

Just at that moment, there was a knock at the front door.

"I wonder who that can be?" Matilda said as she went to look.

It was her best friend Hannah Hedgehog with Bartholomew Badger.

"What lovely presents!" Bartholomew cried as he poked his head round the kitchen door.

"Thank you," replied the happy mouse. "But I do wish I had a Christmas tree for them."

"There are plenty of fir trees in the forest," said Hannah. "Why don't we all go along and find one for you?"

"That's just what we'll do!" Matilda laughed. So the three friends scurried out to the forest.

There was a beautiful little green fir tree, standing right in the middle of the forest.

"That's perfect," Matilda smiled, as she gazed at it. "This tree is definitely the one for me."

3 — Suddenly, however, a tiny robin flew down from the fir tree.

"I've been listening to you all," he cried. "Please don't cut this tree down!"

The three friends *were* surprised.

"I live here with my family," Rusty Robin chirped. "I'd be homeless!"

Before Matilda and her friends had a chance to reply, a friendly squirrel popped up from behind a large red toadstool.

"It's true what Rusty Robin says," Susie Squirrel told them.

4 — "I play in the branches all through summer with my friends. I'd really miss this tree," she added.

All of a sudden, Felicity Fawn pranced over.

"This is a lovely tree," she said shyly. "I love to sit under its shade on a hot day."

The three friends looked at each other.

"How can we possibly cut down the fir tree now?" Matilda said, speaking for them all. "Though I do wish I had somewhere to put my presents, and I do so love putting up all my pretty tree decorations."

Rusty Robin had a wonderful idea.

"Why don't you fetch your decorations and put them on the tree out here?" he suggested.

5 — So the animals hurried back to Matilda's house to fetch the presents. Hannah put all the coloured balls and tinsel into a large box and carried them to the forest.

"This is great fun," Matilda laughed, as she wound some silver tinsel round the branches.

Rusty Robin was given the job of putting the star on the top.

"I can reach more easily," he explained, as he proudly clutched the silver star in his beak.

Soon the decorations were finished, and Bartholomew placed the last parcel under the tree.

"We must all come back here tomorrow morning," Matilda said. "Everyone is invited."

The animals went home feeling very excited that night. They couldn't wait for Christmas Day.

6 — Early on Christmas morning, when the three friends arrived in the forest, they could hardly believe their eyes. The fir tree was lightly covered in snow.

7 — "It's the loveliest Christmas tree," Matilda smiled to herself, joining her chums. And the silver star at the top of the tree twinkled in the sunlight.

Silly Milly's GOOD

Up to four people can play this game, using the counters on the facing page. Throw a dice — the highest score goes first. If there are instructions where you land, follow them. The winner is the player who is first to reach the cinema.

START

1 2 3 4

5
Milly breaks vase while dusting. Finds Mum's lost money inside! Go forward two spaces.

6

7

8
Bring wrong shopping home from supermarket. Go back four spaces to return it.

9

10

11
Milly cleans friend's rabbit hutch. Bunnies escape. Miss a turn.

12 13

14
Baby-sitting cousin Joe but he's brought a video game! Take an extra turn.

15

16